The Sticking Point

BY

Steve Thomson

ISBN 9781849141918

With grateful thanks to Christine, her
colleagues and the
un-named bully who sparked the whole
thing off.

Introduction

Pain.

We all get it.

We all understand it.

What we CAN'T do though is measure it.

We get so used to putting numbers to everything; to putting it on the scales or placing a ruler on it, that it's easy to overlook the fact that pain isn't something that lends itself to being measured.

We can, of course, compare our own experiences: "burning my fingers on a hot pan was less painful than shutting my fingers in the car door, but more painful than stubbing my toe" sort of comparisons, but even these might be flawed since they rely on our memories of these events to be accurate and not to be tempered by time.

In the absence of a scale by which to measure our pain we resort to experience to help us understand the effects of – say – a kick on the shin or a punch on the arm inflicted by another person.

We do this in order to make some sense of the reaction people have to pain, and to anticipate the effects should we decide to kick someone in the shins ourselves, and generally speaking this is the kind of stuff we learn during our childhood.

Pain, as we experience it through our formative years, is about learning and risk assessment.

However, that's all about physical pain.

So what about the other sort of pain? The mental, intellectual or emotional pain that is inflicted upon us and that we often inflict upon others?

This is the kind of pain that comes from rudeness, from bullying –even the most gentle and seemingly innocuous bullying, from bad service, from bad management.

Emotional pain is every bit as real as physical pain, and every bit as debilitating...and it too defies measurement.

There is no means by which we can take an instance of intellectual or emotional pain and decide or establish what it weighs or how tall it is.

So again, as with physical pain, we rely on our memories to provide means by which we can run comparisons, but as with physical pain our memories are subjective and prone to distortion.

There is, however, one significant – indeed huge – difference between physical pain and emotional or mental pain (at least in most societies): we don't go around kicking people, punching them or pinching them. We don't tend to add emphasis to our conversations by slapping the other party or treading on their toes. At the very least such behaviour would be frowned upon, and might well land you in jail!

But emotional pain is different.

It can't be seen; it leaves no bruises; it doesn't draw blood and it doesn't break bones. Only in the most extreme cases might action be taken against someone inflicting such pain, and then often not until it is already too late – the damage is done.

The effect on our minds can be profound. It can change the way we act, how we feel in the morning as we head to work, the path of our relationships. Indeed it can, and I would argue it DOES affect every aspect of our lives, waking and sleeping, 24 hours a day, 365 (or366) days a year every year of our lives.

It's important to recognise that pain isn't a negative thing. This might seem a strange thing to say, but pain is a necessary part of survival. It serves to warn when an experience is potentially or actually damaging to the health and well-being of the individual.

There are a small number of people who are born with a congenital condition (CIPA) which means they are actually unable to experience pain. This might sound great, but it is in fact a huge handicap. The lack of the vital warning signs that pain offers result in these people making extreme physical demands on their bodies, which can and often does result in injuries that most of us would easily avoid. We get the warnings and stop whatever it is – bending our limbs in a particular way for example – while the CIPA sufferer does not 'get the message' and simply keeps bending until eventually a bone breaks or a tendon snaps. Even then, the sufferer may continue to walk on a severely damaged leg, or to carry weights with an arm that has been broken, thereby exacerbating the problem, simply because they do not feel pain. Hence my contention that pain is NOT a negative or pejorative word or experience. It is a message, and an important one.

So what will this book do to help?

Through my work as a trainer and coach I have gained an understanding of the power of visualisation to effect profound changes in people, in their behaviour, their core skills, their ability to communicate and work effectively in a team and much more besides.

With that in mind I would like to offer you a story. A simple tale, but one that carries a key message which you will understand in two distinct ways:

In the first instance, you'll 'get' the story, not as a narrative perhaps – there's not much of a plot or a storyline – but more as a metaphor or allegory, in the manner of 'Who Moved My Cheese' or 'A Pilgrim's Progress'. Secondly, your unconscious mind will 'get' the real message. Once that part of your mind that deals with such things as feelings, emotions, intuition and so forth takes on board the underlying principle of seeing your emotional pain it will move you towards a deeper, more effective and satisfactory method of dealing with that pain as it arises in the transactions we undertake as we go through our lives.

Ultimately, what will happen is that you will be able to see the ebb and flow, the give and take of mental or inner pain as a natural thing, and one which can be easily managed in a way that promotes a balance in your life in all its aspects.

So without any further ado, let's get to the story.

The Sticking Point

The HR manager ushered Leon into what would soon be his workplace, saying as she did:

"It'll be quite a shock to your system, I dare say, working in a place like this after being in a small environment, but I'm sure you'll get used to it in no time at all and feel quite at home."

Two steps into the room Leon stopped in his tracks. The space in which he found himself seemed to go on forever. He could almost swear the furthest corners were shrouded in mist, so far away were they.

"What I'll do – I'll hand you over to Lisa; the office manager. She'll introduce you to a few people, and show you round a bit so you get the feel of the place."

"OK. Thanks," Replied Leon quietly, more than a little intimidated by the sheer scale of his new workplace.

"Lisa, I'd like to introduce you to our newest member of staff. This is Leon, and I thought we could start him over in H12" said the HR lady, with a slight nod in what Leon supposed was the direction of H12.

Lisa stood up with a smile and extended her hand for Leon to shake.

"Welcome to the company Leon. You're going to love it here – we're a friendly bunch, so whatever you need or if you're unsure about anything just ask anyone and they'll help if they can." As she spoke, she ushered Leon round her desk, on which he spotted a neat row of short sticks – about the size of a pencil but rough textured and uneven.

As Leon stepped into the aisle behind Lisa's desk he spotted from the corner of his eye the office manager sweep the small sticks smoothly into her hand and from there into the shallow top drawer of her desk. He wasn't certain, but it looked to him as though the drawer was completely full of similar twigs laid out in neat rows.

[I hope he didn't see them. What happens if he saw them? What will he think? My authority will be completely undermined. Oh I hope he didn't see them!]

Shrugging off the feeling that he had glimpsed something private and maybe even secret, Leon followed the retreating back of his new boss as she strode confidently through the maze of cubicles.

Lisa stopped by a cubicle which to his untutored eye looked much like all the others they had passed, turned back to him with a smile and said:

"Leon, I'd like you to meet Richard, who heads up the procurement team. Richard, this is Leon, who has just started, and will be over in H12"

Richard, who was a small, slightly built man, stood up and the two shook hands. Leon glanced into the cubicle and spotted a pile of the same sort of sticks he had seen on Lisa's desk, but this time they were piled into a neat construction right by Richard's computer monitor. They looked like a Jenga stack, but without the regular smooth finish of the game's pieces, just the rough, natural looking bark of twigs.

Lisa addressed Richard, for a moment ignoring Leon. Her voice took on a slightly haughty tone.

"Richard, I had a call this morning about the C452s you ordered last week. I understand we've had a price rise imposed on us? I should have been told about it direct – not through a third party on another floor! What have you done about sourcing another supplier?"

Richard looked cowed under this onslaught. His shoulders slumped and the smile that had seemed such a natural expression faded into a grimace of discomfort. Leon saw a small movement from the corner of his eye and, turning, glimpsed a couple of those same sticks on Richard's desk. Sticks which he was sure hadn't been there a moment before.

"I'm sorry Lisa. It's not a big price hike and I thought I should just let it ride, as we have a really good relationship with the supplier. If you want, I'll take a look at some of the alternatives and put a report together."

"Do that Richard. And don't just look at *some* of the alternatives. Look at *all* the alternatives and see if you can't save us a bit of money rather than squandering it!"

As Lisa issued this last Parthian shot, already moving away from the small man's desk, Leon saw – actually saw with his own eyes – another of the rough twigs materialise on Richard's desk from nowhere. He looked up and caught Richard's eye. He raised a sympathetic eyebrow, but got no response from the procurement manager who sat down and immediately picked up the new sticks and placed them carefully on the already substantial edifice on his desk.

[That is so unfair! That is just wrong! She shouldn't have said all that in front of the new guy. It's just another example of how unfairly I'm treated all day every day in this place.]

Leon hurried a few steps to catch up with Lisa, bumping a desk corner as he did. The impact was enough to cause a cup of coffee on the desk to slop slightly and a few drops to find their way onto the desk's surface.

"OH FOR GOODNESS SAKE – LOOK AT THIS MESS! " a voice boomed. Startled, Leon half-turned back to see a small woman standing glaring at him from behind the desk he had struck.

"You clumsy PRAT!" she yelled at him in a voice that seemed completely mismatched to her slight frame. "I suppose an APOLOGY would be TOO MUCH TO ASK"

Not sure quite what to do, Leon just stood and stared as the woman started pulling desk drawers open and searching for something while still periodically glaring at him.

Finding his voice, he finally stuttered out an apology, which was ignored by the woman, who had found a tissue amongst her belongings and was swabbing the desk as though it had been swamped by a tidal wave rather than a few drops of coffee. He turned to continue after Lisa, putting his hands in his jacket pockets as he went. His fingers touched something rough and he jerked his hand away before diffidently reaching back in to the pocket and pulling out a twig, exactly like those he had seen earlier. Someone had put a stick in his pocket, presumably while he had been distracted by the angry woman. He left it where he had found it and hurried after his new boss, who was threatening to lose him among the seemingly endless cubicles of the office floor.

"Keep up Leon, we can't have you getting lost before you even get properly started, can we?"

"No...sorry" said Leon, quickening his pace.

Lisa took a sharp right turn, and came to a halt in front of a desk which was dwarfed by an intricate model of what looked to Leon like a church, or maybe a cathedral.

"Wow!" said Lisa. "That's coming on really well Pete. Is there much still to do?"

"Not much" said the desk's occupant: a big man with a shiny domed forehead and a face dominated by a moustache that seemed to have a life of its own, and all but covered his mouth. "Maybe another couple of weeks and it should be done."

"Let me introduce to our latest recruit. Leon, this is Pete, who heads up section G. Pete, this is Leon. He's in H to start with, so you'll no doubt be doing a bit of work together."

"Hi Leon, great to meet you. Once you find your feet, let's get together for a coffee or something and I can show you the ropes. There's so much going on here there's no way your induction will cover it all and Lisa can't tell you everything." Pete's eyes beamed at Leon and the moustache twitched upwards at the ends, so Leon assumed there was a smile lurking in there somewhere.

"Sure" said Leon. "That would be great. I'll look forward to it."

"So...what do you think of this beauty then?" said Pete, gesturing towards the model that dominated his desk.

"It's fantastic...really! Can I ask...what is it a model of?"

"The Basilica of St Peter in Rome – well, Vatican City really, but you know what I mean."

"It's awesome. What's it made from?"

Pete looked up from his model with a surprised look on his face.

"Pain sticks of course." He said, as though this was self-evident. "What else would I be using?" He added with a laugh.

[What's this kid on, for goodness sake? What's it made from indeed! What does he think, I'm bringing twigs I from the park or something? Still, no-one's being of much help in getting this beauty finished, so maybe twigs would be a good idea...no...it wouldn't be right. It would feel like cheating.

Maybe I ought to mess up on something – get people to pay me a little attention...garner a few more pain sticks...get this sucker finished finally]

Leon smiled noncommittally, and sketched a small wave by way of taking his leave of a man who gave all the appearances of being normal, but was evidently as daft as a bed-bug. "Pain sticks?" Leon asked himself under his breath. "What's he on?"

He looked round for Lisa, but was dismayed to find that she had disappeared without trace. Taking a stab at the direction he should be taking he soldiered on, sure that he would find her in a cubicle along the way chatting with one or other of his new colleagues.

Doubts started to creep in when, after walking for a minute or two, he still hadn't come across her. He thought of asking someone in one of the workspaces he passed, but like most men he was happier carrying on and trusting to luck than being seen to need help from strangers.

Hearing raised voices coming from a cubicle a little further along the aisle down which he was walking, Leon hurried towards the sounds, feeling sure that Lisa would be one of the protagonists. From what little he had seen so far, she wasn't a person to be taken lightly, and apparently had no compunction about telling her staff what they should or shouldn't be doing.

When he stepped into the entrance to the cubicle from which the noises had come though, it wasn't Lisa he found, but two people virtually nose-to-nose, each talking over the other, and neither apparently listening to anything the other had to say. At their feet lay a pile of the mystery sticks.

As his figure cast a shadow over the two, they stopped their argument and turned as one towards him.

"Yes?" said a youngish man in shirtsleeves and an open-collar, not bothering to modify his tone from that of the argument.

"Sorry to interrupt" he said "I was looking for Lisa"

"Haven't seen her." he turned to the other protagonist – a woman. "You?" he asked, his tone becoming more gentle.

"Nope. Haven't seen her all morning. Sorry." She turned away from Leon, as though he had already disappeared. Turning back to the young man, she started where she had evidently left off.

"You better get it finished before lunch, or Neil is going to hear about it."

"Fine!" was the response. "I'll tell him myself right now" He reached for the phone on the desk which took up most of the cubicle's space and lifted the receiver. Immediately the woman's hand came down on his and slammed the phone back onto its base.

"NO!" she all but shouted. "I'll tell him."

"Whatever" said the young man, heading straight for Leon, who was still filling the gap that constituted the only way in or out of the space. "'Scuse me." he muttered as he brushed past him.

"Where the hell do you think *you're* going?"

"Coffee break" came the reply from a rapidly departing figure.

"Bum, bum, bum!" Said the young woman, rubbing her face with her hands. "This is all going to land on me, I bloody know it!" She walked round the desk and fell into the chair behind it. Leon sidled deeper into the workspace and cleared his throat. She lifted her head and looked at him from under a fringe of dark hair.

"You're still here? I thought you were looking for Lisa. Who are you anyway?"

"Ah...yes...sorry. Still here." Leon's gaze flitted around the small space, as though looking for inspiration.

"And?"

"And what? Sorry."

"Who are you? And please don't start your reply with another apology."

"No...sorry. Oops, sorry. Sorry. Leon. I'm Leon. I'm new."

"Sorry Leon. Sorry, sorry Leon. Good name. Is it one sorry or two?"

"Sor...No, just Leon." He replied, finally getting the hang of it.

"OK just Leon. What can I do for you since I can't magic Lisa up for you?

Leon paused. Maybe this was his chance to find out about the sticks. There was only one way to find out.

"What's with these?" He poked the pile of twigs with his toe, setting up a small avalanche as he did so.

"Sorry?" She said, and immediately blushed a little. "I mean, what do you mean 'what's with...?"

Leon found her last sentence a little complicated, and had to translate it in his head before venturing an answer.

"I mean...what ARE these?"

The girl looked baffled "Huh?" was the best she could manage in reply.

"Everyone's got them. Since I came in here this morning, everyone's got some stash of these things. Someone even stuck one in my pocket." He delved into his jacket to find the item in question, only to discover that he now had three. It didn't seem likely that they were breeding, so someone must have slipped a couple more in there while he was distracted. He pulled all three out and showed the young woman. "Look...three of them. Three."

"Yes, I can see that." She seemed hesitant. "But so what?"

"So what? So what?" Leon's voice went into a very high register, which tended to happen when he got excited or angry, much to his own discomfort.

"Woah! Dog whistle or what?" Was the response. And no sooner had the words left her mouth than another stick appeared right on Leon's hand as he was watching. He dropped all four as though they were on fire.

"Did you see that? Did you SEE that? It just...appeared out of nowhere!"

"You...you're weird!" said the girl, with an expression on her face that lay somewhere in the area between puzzled, amused and worried. She knelt down and gathered up the four sticks, handing them back to him. Reluctantly, he took them from her.

"I'm weird? It's not me that treats stuff falling out of the sky as normal! I'm not the one building churches out of sticks that just appear from nowhere!"

The girl just looked at him, with a quick glance at the exit to make sure she could make a run for it if Leon started to look dangerous.

Almost in tears of frustration, Leon pleaded with her: "Just tell me what's going on...PLEASE."

Straightening up, the girl thrust out her hand, smiling, and said "HI, I'm Annie" as though they were meeting socially. Leon automatically responded with a handshake, "Leon" he said.

"Good. Leon. I know. Great to meet you" she said, still acting as though they were in the kitchen at a party where they didn't know anyone.

"Likewise" said Leon, now adding bafflement at her behaviour to the emotions that were already at play in response to the sudden appearance of the fourth stick.

[I get it. He's been sent by the company to check us out. Some sort of psychometric test or something. I need to play along. Take it where he leads me and hope it's what they're looking for. Who knows: it might be a promotion thing.]

"So...Leon. What can I help you with?"

"These" said Leon, indicating the pile of wood on the floor of the cubicle. "Tell me about these."

"Sure. These are pain sticks. We get them if we experience pain." She smiled, as though that sentence had made some sort of sense, which, at least to Leon's mind, it hadn't.

"But I've not been hurt. No-one's touched me. How do I come to have four of them?"

"Not that sort of pain. That's what bruises are for, and bleeding. These are for the other kind of pain."

Leon's blank expression led her to continue. "Mental pain. Emotional stuff. Bullying or rudeness or...I dunno...bad service. That sort of thing."

"No...I don't get it. Sorry"

[Maybe he's had a knock on the head. Maybe he's got amnesia or something. Well, whether it's that or he's a spy I'd better humour him.]

So, OK. Let's see if I can explain this.

[How do you explain it? It's like explaining breathing or your pulse.]

"So...what was your name again?"

"Leon" said Leon.

Annie. Pleased to meet you We've already done that bit ?"

e did that...twice I think." was the subdued reply.

"Well never mind." said the woman in a brisk fashion. "You want to know about pain sticks?"

"Yes...please...sorry..."

"Back to the apologies eh? Never mind. Soooo...pain sticks...I don't know where to start really." she paused, a little frown appearing on her brow as she pondered on the problem "Give me your hand." she said after a few seconds.

Leon held out his left hand and she took it, turning it palm side up. She took a gentle but firm hold of his thumb and folded it in towards the palm. Suddenly, and without warning she pressed the thumb hard, squeezing it back towards Leon's wrist, wringing a sharp cry of pain from the young man.

"What the hell was that for?" he demanded.

"What did that feel like?" came back Annie

Painful! Really painful."

She landed a solid punch on his arm, just below the shoulder.

"OW! Bloody hell!"

"What did THAT feel like then?" asked Annie

"A bit sore. You surprised me"

"Which hurt more?

"The thing with the thumb. It was like torture or something."

"Yeah, I learned it in self-defence class. 'How to overwhelm a larger opponent' I think it was, anyway the point is, they both hurt, right? The punch and the thumb thing?"

"Yes"

But I don't know *how much* they hurt, because I'm not you, and you're not me. There's no way to measure how big or small, how light or heavy the pain is. Do you see?"

"Yes, I guess" said Leon "but I don't really get your point."

"Stay with me Leon, I'm doing my best here. Think about this: *you* can measure your own pain...sort of...by comparing it with what you've experienced in the past, but you can't show anyone else how big or small it is, you can only show them the bruise, or the blood or the scar."

"OK, I think I see what you're getting at, but I still don't see what that has to do with these" he said, extending the hand holding his four sticks towards her.

"I'm getting to that. So far, what I've been talking about is the physical pain of being punched or cutting yourself or being hit by a bus or something. But what about mental pain? Emotional pain? Intellectual pain? It's just as real as the physical stuff, but if it wasn't for pain sticks it would be invisible too! No blood, no bruises. How would you know if you had hurt someone? How could you get any idea of what harm you were causing? So what we have are these – pain sticks. You get one when something or someone gives you mental pain." She smiled at him with a sort of *Ta-Daa!* Look, as though she really has explained the phenomenon to him.

"Look, I'm sorry. I mean I get what you're saying about the pain and stuff, but where do these things come from? They can't just...*appear.*"

"Well of course they can. How else do they get here? When someone's rude to you, or bullies you or ignores you or whatever...a pain stick appears. It just does." Annie said this as though she was answering a question like 'why is the sky?'

[This is crazy! How long is he going to keep this up? Any time now he's going to tell me that he was sent by HR to test me on how I deal with nutters or something]

"Look" said Leon "I know you must be thinking I'm a madman. It's just that...I've never heard of pain sticks. I've never seen one appear out of thin air. In fact, I've never seen *anything* appear out of thin air before I got here this morning! This is all just too weird. Maybe I *am* going mad."

Something in his tone made Annie mentally step back and make a rapid re-evaluation. She took stock of Leon's appearance, taking in the clearly new but cheap and rather ill-fitting jacket, the wrinkled shirt and a tie that may well have had its knot made up once and then carefully retained for some years. She saw the shoes that were clearly purchased with comfort in mind rather than style. A glance at his hair made it obvious that he had wrestled into some sort of order, but that its natural preference would be to run a bit wild and free. She looked at his face and saw only sincerity and worry in his expression. Either he was a master of disguise and a world-class actor or he genuinely was what he professed to be: someone who had no knowledge of one of the most fundamental elements of everyday life. In other words a nutter – though of course she would never say such a thing out loud...or at least not to him. After all, how would he react to another pain stick dropping on him when he was so obviously distressed by the meagre handful he had already accrued since he got to the office.

What she was to do next was a puzzle. She could make an excuse and leave him to wander the office alone, getting into who knows *what* kind of bother and maybe getting himself or someone else hurt, she could stall him and find a way to make a call to security – let *them* deal with it, or since he seemed unlikely to actually turn violent, and he wasn't totally repulsive to look at and he didn't smell or anything, she could continue to humour him, walk him through the office and show him the sights. Doubtless Lisa would eventually come looking for him anyway and would then relieve her of the chaperone duties. She ran through a mental checklist of what she had to get done during the course of the day, and reckoned that an hour or so could be devoted to a bit of care in the community work.

"OK Leon. Here's what we'll do: I'll show you round and introduce you to a few people, and I'll explain about the pain sticks on one condition."

"Sure...what?"

"You don't...under any circumstances...say *anything* to *anyone* about not knowing what pain sticks are. Understood? If you say *one word* to anyone other than me, not only will I disown you but you'll probably find yourself on the way to a secure hospital within the hour. Are we clear on this?"

"Crystal" replied Leon "Not a word."

"OK, we can start here" she nodded towards the floor and the pile of sticks that lay there.

"So...these are yours?" Asked Leon, keen to at least seem to be grasping the concept, though in fact he was still completely baffled.

"Well, yes and no" said Annie "they're a bit Simon's..."

"The guy who was here with you?" asked Leon.

"Yes. Anyway, some of these are his, some are mine, and in a way some aren't really anyone's."

"I'd like to say that I know what you're talking about, but that would be a lie. It sounds even more complicated than you made it out to be."

"You're right. Maybe this isn't the best place to start. This is a pretty strange situation - not something you'd come across every day for sure. Nonetheless, I'm going to try to explain, and maybe if I can't make it clear we can come back to it later. So what was happening when you walked in was that I had asked Simon to run an audit on some stock and he said no. So, I had one drop on me..."

"A pain stick you mean?"

"Yeah, we talk about getting one dropped on us or dropping one on someone. That sort of thing. You'll hear it a lot. Anyway, I had one drop on me, so I said that he had to do it because the request had come from above."

What...from the same place as the pain sticks come from?"

"No, you moron. From my boss! I'm Simon's line manager, and so when MY line manager told me he needed an audit done today I naturally came down to get Simon on the case."

"Only he said no, right?" put in Leon, to show he was listening.

"Uh-huh. He said he didn't have the time. And I have to say that I agree with him. If he's going to get his regular work done he doesn't have time to do this audit today. But as it was a direct instruction from MY boss I had to insist...which dropped a couple on Simon. He then reminded me that when he started working here there were two other people in the department, so three of them doing what Simon does on his own now."

"What happened to the other two?"

"One retired and Simon was asked to take on her role as well as his own. He got a raise of course."

"Oh, of course" This interjection got a sharp look from Annie, and Leon found himself to be in possession of yet another of the sticks. "Sorry" he said quietly.

She continued: "So then there were two, and everything was going along fine, when Simon's assistant decided to get pregnant and leave...and wasn't replaced. Simon therefore was left with the work of three people."

"But with a raise" put in Leon.

"You're sounding sarcastic Leon, and that could be very hurtful. And if I suddenly find that I'm getting sticks dropping on me because I'm hurt by your thoughtless comments. You'll be finding out about how it all works from a very first-hand place indeed. Am I making myself clear?"

"Ah...yes. Sorry."

"And STOP BLOODY APOLOGISING!"

"Oops" said Leon.

"So, back to the matter in hand. I'm asking Simon to do something for which he has no time. Simon is refusing. Secretly I'm agreeing with Simon that he shouldn't even be asked to do this stuff, least of all at short notice, and we're both slagging each other off. So we're dropping sticks on each other, but we're also having them drop on us - because we both think and feel that the whole situation is deeply unfair. The upshot of which is that while we had all these drop on us" she poked a toe at the pile of twigs - "neither of us really feels as though they are ours, so we don't really need to keep them or find something to do with them."

"Got it...I think" said Leon.

"OK. Let's head out and I'll show you how it all works." Annie headed towards the main office, but Leon paused.

"Aren't you going to take them with you?" he asked, nodding towards the sticks.

"Nope." she replied. "I'll leave them there for now. The ones that don't belong to anyone will disappear in a while; Simon will come back from his break and do whatever he does with his, and I'll pick up the rest later on. Now come on. I haven't got all day!"

Leon, still clutching his four sticks, followed.

Speaking over her shoulder as she walked, Annie started to explain:

"People have different ways of dealing with their sticks. That's really what it's all about. Some folk ignore them, some people stack them up and examine them...though I don't know what they expect to see...when you've seen one pain stick you've pretty much seen them all. There are people who just love to show you their collections, others who are ashamed of theirs....it's endless! A world of pain and a world of dealing with it."

[Annie: That was pretty profound. I'm going to have to remember that and write it down when I get rid of this guy.]

"Let's start with Veronique. She transferred here from the Lyon office last year, and the rumour is that she was given the chance to move because everyone in the French operation was sick of listening to her moan. I don't know how much truth there is in that, but I can certainly see how it might happen. She's caught in a vicious circle: She moans about how much grief she gets from everyone and how many sticks she has dropped on her all the time, which winds people up, so they're less polite to her than they might be...and that there is what we in the trade call an understatement...which of course causes sticks to rain down on her, which she collects, and then shows everyone, letting them know how very unfair life is, which makes people more inclined to be rude to her, and so she gets sticks....you get the idea, I'm sure. Let's go meet her." Annie headed off to her left and then took a quick right into a cubicle filled in equal measure by a large woman and an even larger stack of the now familiar pain sticks. The woman was of indeterminate age, dressed in what to some might pass as timeless elegance, but to others would merely be a frumpy twin-set, and exuded a strong scent of lavender and mothballs.

"Hi Veronique" said Annie in a voice so full of good cheer and bonhomie that Leon for a moment assumed that the two were best friends.

"Oh hi Annie" came the reply, in a small voice that didn't fit the large frame of the woman at the desk at all. "I hope you haven't come with more work from Neil. I've hardly started the last batch he sent down, and it's all so awful! He emails all the time asking for it and asking why it's taking so long, but he doesn't *know* how much work I have to do, and every time he calls or emails I get so *upset...*you know? *So* upset...that it takes me some time to calm down, and of course that puts me further behind. Maybe you can tell him how *much* I have to do, and make him leave me alone for just a *few minutes* to get on with it. Can you, Annie? Please?"

"I haven't brought any more work, but Veronique, the last stuff Neil sent you came down here over three weeks ago, and there wasn't that much. You should have been able to get rid of it in an afternoon."

The large woman seemed to shrink inside her cashmere, and her already small voice shrank with her.

"It's all so bloody awful. No-one will help me." Suddenly, she stood up and strode over to the imposing pile of pain sticks that dominated her office. She stooped down and ran her fingers through them, scooping them up and throwing them into the air.

"Look!" she demanded "Look at all this! This is what I have to put up with! People demanding things that are unreasonable. People being rude and obnoxious! People sniggering at me behind my back! Every day

44

I collect more and more of these...these...*Paah!"* She threw a handful of sticks at the wall of her cubicle and slumped back into her chair, putting her impeccable hairdo at risk by laying her head on her folded arms, her voice mumbling on, "So unfair. Everyone is laughing and giving me more to do...so unfair..."

Annie signalled to Leon that they should leave, and the two tiptoed out into the aisle, then walked swiftly away from the still audible series of complaints.

"Shouldn't we be helping her or something? She looks to be in a bit of a state," said Leon.

"Don't worry. As soon as she's sure we're out of earshot she'll be on the phone moaning to Neil about how unfair I am and how demanding. Every visitor to her workspace gets the same show – the moaning – all the business of throwing the sticks around – the works. In fact, she could get rid of the whole pile of sticks if she wanted, but then she wouldn't be able to do the whole drama queen thing."

"How would she get rid of them then?"

Loads of ways. The simplest would be to be nice to everyone, and to be accommodating when someone asked her to do something. Every time she smiled and said 'No problem' or something, some of the sticks would go. Pretty soon she'd be in the same place as the rest of us, with sticks coming and going but never building up the way hers have."

Leon, still nearly sure that he was going to wake up soon and find out that this whole episode was just a pepperoni pizza giving him nightmares, nonetheless saw a flaw in what Annie was saying.

"How come I saw a guy with enough sticks to build a model of St Peter's? Shouldn't they have been disappearing and leaving him with a ruin?"

"Ah...you mean Pete and his famous Basilica. No...when you're doing something constructive with your painsticks they hang around. They come and go when you're...I don't know what the right phrase is...in balance, I guess. You'll see as we go round." She sped up, forcing Leon to stride after her, only to stop suddenly, causing him to crash into her back, and all but knock her over.

"Bloody hell Leon! Look where you're going!"

Leon sensed the arrival of yet another stick in his jacket pocket and reached in to grasp it. "Sorry."

"Uh-oh...Sorry Leon's back in town." Came the reply with a smile. The stick which had dropped on Leon disappeared from his hand. The look on his face told Annie what had happened.

"See? Balance. I shout at you for being clumsy – painstick drops on you. I forgive you with a wee smile - painstick goes." The smile she bestowed on Leon warmed him, and when she reached out and grabbed his arm, pulling him close to her. He almost forgot that he was going mad and came close to enjoying himself.

"C'mon. In here." said Annie, pulling Leon into a space that he saw was different from the workstations he had visited. It was laid out as a small lounge area, with a coffee machine and a snack vending machine against one wall, a low cupboard against another, a small table in the middle of the floor and a handful of easy chairs dotted around.

"We can get a bit of a view from here. Give me a hand with this." She grasped one side of the table and Leon took the other. She led him towards the cupboard, and set the table down alongside it, quickly stepping up onto it and from there to the top of the cabinet. She reached a hand down to Leon, and helped him balance as he followed her route.

"Look over there" she pointed over the wall. Leon followed her instruction and gazed out over a maze of partitions and aisles, the tops of heads visible in some of the workspaces and a few figures walking through the vast space.

"What am I looking at?" he asked. She stepped behind him, leaning close and laid her arm on his shoulder so he could sight down it.

"There...over there. Do you see that column?"

"Yes...I see it. So what?"

Look around. Do you see any other columns in here?"

Doing as he was bid, Leon realised that she was quite right. No other columns to be seen.

"It's not a column" she said "It's a model."
Leon half turned to look at her.

"A model of what? A column?"

"Nope...it's a model of a Saturn 5 rocket. The same rocket that took Apollo 11 to the moon."

"Get out of here!" said Leon. "You're pulling my leg."

"No, seriously. It's the pride and joy of the Research and Development guys. It's taken them years to build. And you can only see a part of it from here. They cut a hole in the ceiling, and the floor. It goes up another two floors and down one...or maybe two. It's a 1:10 scale model."

"And it's made of sticks?"

"Uh-huh. Thousands...maybe millions of sticks. All the sticks that have been dropped on them since they started to build it...before I even came to work here. They even had to get the New Product Development department downstairs moved from 2G13 to where they are now in 2S4 so that they could get it all lined up and joined together." She jumped down from the cupboard to the table and then to the floor, beckoning him to follow.

"We can go and visit them if you want. They always have good coffee over there."

"Sure. After you." said Leon, and the two headed in the direction of the scientists' lair.

Annie seemed to be in something of a hurry to get to the area of the office that was dominated by the great model rocket, and though Leon would have liked to have asked her questions about some of the things he glimpsed as they walked she ignored his occasional attempts to talk. He made a mental note of a few of the more bizarre or puzzling things he noticed – in fact, as he passed more and more cubicles, he realised that he was seeing everything in relation to the painsticks that were on show, and if none were visible, he fell to wondering what the owner did with them.

Before too long, the pair reached an area of open floor which, though not really large was, by the standards of the rest of the office, a veritable savannah.

"This is where the real world stops and the wacky world of R&D begins" Annie said, with a wave of her arm to indicate the empty floor. Leon smiled to himself at the phrase 'the real world', believing as he did that he was dreaming and would...soon hopefully...wake to the *real,* real world, where sticks didn't appear in your hand and people didn't use twigs for anything more complicated than playing Pooh-sticks with their children or scraping dog crap from the soles of their trainers.

"Let's see if we can find a tame geek and get him to tell you about the rocket" said Annie, interrupting Leon's thoughts.

"Whatever you say" he replied with a smile, and followed her across the empty carpet towards the towering column which Leon could now see was indeed constructed of countless thousands of the gnarley twigs that were so much a part of this world.

It didn't take long to find someone to talk to. A youngish man with all the hallmarks of a classic geek – the high forehead, thinning and deeply unfashionable hair, a breast pocket with pens tucked into it, he had obviously come straight from Central Casting to play the part of '2nd scientist'.

Annie accosted the man as he crossed their path.

"I wonder if you can help me" she said "My name's Annie. I work over in Stats, and I'm showing our newest recruit here" she waved a hand in Leon's direction "a few of the more interesting sights around the office – introducing him to some of the folk he'll be working with. That kind of thing, and he asked me about the rocket, so I brought him over to see it close up." She finished this bending of the truth with a sweet smile which Leon was sure would have melted his heart if it had been pointed at him. The effect it had on the young scientist certainly looked as though his temperature might get high enough to melt the pens in his pocket, if not his heart. He blushed a deep burgundy red and took a small step backwards.

"Wah..wah...what...who..." was the reply.

"This is Leon" again with a wave in his general direction "and I'm sorry, I didn't catch your name.."

Uh...Ellis. Muh...my name is Ellis." came the mumbled response.

"Oh! Nice name! Is that a first name or a surname?"

"Buh...both. Ellis Ellis. My name. Ellis Ellis."

Ellis Ellis was making some sort of recovery from the scare of being addressed by a good looking woman and the colour was slowly fading from his cheeks.

Annie positively beamed with delight at this revelation "Ellis Ellis! That is so *cool!* Ellis Ellis.*" She said it as though she was tasting it for sweetness. "Well I hope you won't mind if I call you Ellis" she added with a laugh. Ellis snickered rather than laughed, but it was apparently OK for Annie to call him whatever she wanted – he wasn't going to be complaining.

"So...Ellis" said Annie, taking him gently by the elbow and steering him in the direction of the rocket "maybe we could sit somewhere and Leon could ask some of the questions he has about this fantastic model. Would that be OK?" she sounded as though she was talking to a five-year-old, but Ellis seemed not to notice and merely tagged along where she led him, nodding agreement. Leon couldn't help but spot that the man's lab coat pocket was pretty well loaded up with painsticks and he wondered briefly if it was Annie's rather patronising tone that had called them down from wherever they emanated, but then decided that it was more likely that the scientist had brought them on himself. Maybe it would be possible to ask him sometime,

"Ellis" he said, once the trio were sitting in a spare cubicle "Tell me about the rocket...or, no...tell me about how you got enough painsticks to *build* the rocket."

"Oh the sticks were *no* problem. We're in research and development, so we come up with all *sorts* of crap ideas that get shot down in flames as soon as we present them. I reckon that we can gather as many as three or four hundred sticks in one presentation, if we get all the top guys in the company along at the same time. More often it's about 80 or 90. But then, we make quite a few presentations, so it all adds up."

Leon looked at Ellis in amazement, while Annie clapped her hands and cheered quietly.

"Way to go, Ellis!"

"So...you purposely develop things you know are useless just to get more sticks?" asked Leon.

"Oh yeah. Though of course we do have some decent ideas too...obviously, or we'd all get fired. We've come up with some real winners in amongst all the rubbish. And to be honest, the ratio of good ideas to bad ones isn't *that* much different from any other big corporate R&D department."

[*Ellis: I wish these guys would finish up and leave me alone. I've got so much to do. I need to write a whole report on a fictitious pet food supplement in time for tomorrow's meeting, and if I don't get it done in time we'll fall behind schedule on getting the fuel pump assembly built, then we'll have the guys down in New Product Development on our case...which will give us some sticks, but not nearly enough!*

Annie spoke up with a big grin on her face.

"When do you think it'll be finished?"

"Oh, not for a while. We've got some plans that'll take a bit of work to get through."

"Plans?"

"I can't tell you too much. It's a secret, but I *can* tell you that we're not just building a model of a big metal tube now, we're going to be adding some stuff to the original idea...some stuff to go *inside* the rocket."

"What do you mean 'inside'?"

"I mean...we're going to build an *engine!*"

"Do *what*?" said Leon, while Annie's jaw dropped in astonishment.

"We're going to make it a *working* model! Of course, this'll mean we need to gather a whole lot more sticks, but we've got it covered. We're going to pitch a complete set of concept products that will absolutely give us all the sticks we could ever need!"

Annie asked: "What sort of products are we talking about here Ellis?"

"This is all confidential, yeah? You promise you won't tell anyone? I shouldn't really be talking about this stuff, but I'm...I *trust* you guys." He wasn't looking at Leon when he said this, and it was clear that what he meant was that he *wanted* to trust Annie.

"Of course you can trust us" said Annie, leaning forward and putting a hand on Ellis's knee. "We won't breath a word. We wouldn't even be here if it wasn't for Leon being so interested in the rocket." She sounded so sincere that both Leon and Ellis believed her absolutely...despite the fact that Leon for one knew that she was, if not exactly lying, at the very least bending the facts a little. He also realised that as a result of her patience in telling him about painsticks he now knew that were he to call her out on the little white lies she was telling, she'd be the proud owner of a few more of them...and -- he also saw -- Ellis Ellis would also have a small contribution towards getting his rocket finished, as a result of having his trust in Annie proven to be unfounded. However (he suddenly realised) letting Annie down by giving the game away would also bring down more than a couple of the damn sticks on Leon himself, and he, unlike Ellis and his geek pals, didn't have a nice little hobby like a Saturn rocket on which he could use his sticks, so he had no real idea of what he could do to get rid of them. No, he'd be left holding them or sticking them in his pockets...there was no doubt in his mind – he was going to have to find a way to offload them...some way to make them disappear...use them...something. As these thoughts rolled through his mind, he realised that he was starting to treat all this as if it were real. As though he wasn't in the middle of a particularly vivid dream. What was he doing worrying about what he was going to do with his painsticks, when he would soon be waking up in his own bed and would never see another painstick as long as he lived...he hoped!

As Leon turned thoughts of painsticks over and over in his head, Annie continued to quiz Ellis Ellis.

"What sort of thing are you planning on pitching, then?" she asked.

The young scientist's answer brought Leon back to what he supposed passed for reality.

"Planned obsolescence" he exclaimed.

Annie looked puzzled, and Leon was surprised. It was Leon who spoke first.

"How are you going to make *that* sound like something new?"

Annie continued to look puzzled, and this time Ellis joined in, looking just as quizzical as she did.

"What are you talking about? We've only just come up with the concept...*and* the name!"

This time it was Leon's turn to do the 'puzzled' thing, while Annie kept up her perfect record by maintaining the same bemused expression she had worn since the phrase 'planned obsolescence' was first uttered.

"But..." said Leon "Things are *always* breaking down 20 minutes after the guarantee runs out. It's what stuff *does*."

Seeing Ellis once again join Annie in the now familiar state of befuddlement, Leon gave up trying to understand what was going on, and decided to let the scientist tell them what was planned. It seemed the only way they were going to move the conversation forward.

"I don't know what *you* think it means, but what *we've* decided to pitch is a range of products that are planned to wear out! Think about *that*!"

With a sigh, Leon gave a nod. "Tell me more."

"We're going to pitch car tyres that need to be replaced every 15,000 kilometres. We're going to tell them about lightbulbs that stop working after a while...I can't remember exactly how long...five years maybe? We'll show them prototypes of a razor that goes blunt after it's been used a few times. There's more too...*loads* of things. Chewing gum that loses its flavour after a few minutes. *All sorts* of stuff. So you see? They'll laugh us out of the boardroom, and we'll end up having about a *million* sticks drop on us. We'll have the engine built in *no* time!"

Annie just shook her head slowly from side to side.

"That's amazing." she said, in a voice filled with awe. "You guys are *mental.*"

"What if they like them?" asked Leon quietly

"*Like* them*?*" said Ellis "How could anyone *like* them? They're *stupid* ideas.. They make no sense."

"They make sense if you get profits by selling the lightbulbs, the tyres and the rest. They make perfect sense if people have to buy something over and over again, and each time they do, you – the company that is – makes a little bit more money. They make sense *then* Ellis. Don't you see?"

"But that's nuts. Why would anyone buy something that wears out when they already have something that's perfectly good?"

"First, you tell them in your advertising that they can't live without these amazing new tyres or whatever, then you stop making the old ones."

But other companies will just make the proper tyres, so no-one will buy the stupid tyres."

"Until the other companies see what you're doing, and that you're making profits by doing it, then they'll *all* want a piece of it, and the world will never see an indestructible tyre or razor or whatever ever again! Is that what you want Ellis? Is that what you want to pitch, just so you can build your stupid rocket? If it is, then go right ahead, because I can promise you one thing: there'll be a hell of a lot of painsticks coming your way if you do. Yours and everyone else's. We'll all be up to our *eyes* in painsticks and you'll be needing your rocket then Ellis, and you'll need it to have an engine too, and furthermore you'd better plan on packing a map of the cosmos with some decent planets marked on it as well. Pack an overnight bag Ellis...you'll want to take a wee trip, old son, because we'll all be pretty keen to talk to the bright sparks that thought up *'planned obsolescence'* , that's for sure. We'll *all* want to have a quiet word about *that* little gem of an idea!"

Ellis backed away from Leon, who had been leaning forward and jabbing at him with a rigid finger throughout this diatribe. His movement brought him hard up against Annie, who had been uncharacteristically silent throughout the exchange. She pushed him firmly away with an open hand.

"Thanks for filling us in Ellis. I appreciate your taking the time to talk to us. I think I should, however, tell you that we are in fact from internal security and have been conducting an undercover enquiry into certain...shall we call them *dubious* work practices that have been brought to our attention. Naturally, we will have to prepare a report, and I expect you'll get a call from HR in due course. In the meantime, I suggest you get back to work...your *proper* work, that is, immediately!" With this, she turned on her heel and marched away in the direction from which they had arrived. "Come on Leon" she called over her shoulder as she strode away. Leon heard a loud groan and a clattering noise behind him, and, turning to see what had caused it, was just in time to see the hapless scientist being swamped beneath a torrent of well-deserved painsticks. "Serves you right, mate, and I hope your geeky pals got some too!" He lengthened his stride and quickly caught up with his fellow 'undercover operative', who surprised him more than a little by turning to him and catching him in a hug, burying her face into his chest. His first thought was that she was crying, but when she moved away slightly to catch her breath it was laughter that was causing her shoulders to shake rather than tears. She dragged a deep breath into her lungs without relinquishing her hold on him and, leaning back a little so that she could look him in the eye.

"Did you see his face? Did you see the look on his face? Poor Ellis Ellis. I almost feel sorry for him." She seemed to sober up a little at this thought. "What are they *thinking* about over there?"

"I don't know," said Leon "but I know for sure that Ellis Ellis will be trying to talk them out of whatever it is...just as soon as he can dig himself out from under the pile of sticks you dropped on him."

"Me? I didn't drop *nearly* as many on him as *you* did. You probably dropped enough on him to get his stupid engine built!" At this thought she started giggling again, and her arms tightened round the young man...something he found to be very much to his liking.

At the thought of how good it felt to be held by an attractive young woman, another thought struck Leon. He extricated one arm and felt in his jacket pocket for the painsticks he had had drop on him since his arrival, only to find the pocket empty...and he started to think that he was perhaps beginning to get a grasp of the whole painstick concept.

After a few all too brief seconds (at least from Leon's point of view) Annie let her arms fall to her sides, and Leon, taking the hint, also relinquished his embrace.

"So..." said Annie, "let's get on, shall we? Plenty more to see, plenty more to try to explain...I take it you're going to keep up this pantomime of not knowing about painsticks?"

"Annie, I wouldn't lie to you. It's no joke. I really don't know about them. Really."

"OK. I'll play along. C'mon." She took his hand and headed off down yet another of the aisles that seemed to his eye to be indistinguishable from any of the others he had explored, either with Lisa or latterly with Annie. Looking over his shoulder, he took a last look at the towering edifice of Ellis's rocket and allowed himself to be led onwards.

"If I take you at your word, and assume that you really don't understand one of the fundamental principles of life – namely painsticks – then there are a handful of people I need you to see before we get you to your cubicle, or before we bump into Lisa. Whichever comes first. Up here on the right is someone that I don't think you should meet, but I think you should sneak a peek at as we pass. His name is David. He's worked here all his life. He came here from school and met his wife here (she worked in logistics). They were inseparable. Ate lunch together every day, that kind of thing. He could have had a promotion a while back, but it would have meant relocating, and she wasn't able to get a transfer straight away, though she would probably have been able to move across in a few months. That wasn't good enough though. They couldn't imagine being apart for months, even if he were able to come home at weekends. So he turned down the promotion. Stayed here with her. No kids, just the two of them."

"So...?" asked Leon.

"She died. Turned out she had pancreatic cancer which wasn't diagnosed until it was already pretty advanced. When the doctors finally spotted it, they only had a matter of months together before she passed away. This was about a year ago I suppose. He was wiped out, but he insisted on coming back to work pretty much straight away. Said it was the only thing that would keep his mind off it, but that was never going to happen. He works, but he's so completely immersed in the past and so distraught about the present and what the future will be like that it's hard to see how he keeps going."

She put a finger to her lips to indicate that they should be quiet, and drew to a halt at a point by the corner of another of the anonymous workspaces. She leaned in to him and standing on tiptoe breathed into his ear...

"This is his cubicle. Listen..."

Leon held his breath for a moment, and heard a low voice from behind the grey partition.

"It's so unfair...you should never have been taken. There are so many people in this world that are worth so much less than you. So unfair..."

Once again Annie pressed close to Leon – something from which he was beginning to take great pleasure – and spoke quietly "When we walk past, take a quick peek in, OK?"

"Sure" he responded.

The two locked step, with Annie once again taking his hand in hers, and they walked past the entrance to the work station. As they passed, Leon got a quick glimpse of the man he assumed was David, sitting with his chin on his forearms, which lay across his desk. He was talking quietly, apparently addressing a photograph of a pleasant looking woman – his late wife, Leon guessed. The desk, the floor and every horizontal surface of the cubicle was heaped high with painsticks.

They had passed the entrance and were a little further down the corridor before Annie broke the silence.

"Did you see?"

"Yes" replied Leon "but I'm not sure what to make of it. I mean, he's lost his wife, so he's in pain and gets a bunch of sticks dropped on him. If painsticks are real, then that's more or less what I'd expect, surely."

"Yes...sort of. But consider this: when someone dies, they're gone, right? And whether you think that's it, or you think they've gone to some paradise or heaven or somewhere you don't imagine them being in pain do you? No," she said, answering her own question, "you think of them being at peace somewhere...or just gone. It's the people left behind that feel the pain. The pain of loss, of grief, of being abandoned or of having their loved-one taken from them by someone or something stronger than themselves or by something sneaky and nasty and dark. But pain is pain, so no matter who or what David is blaming for the loss of his wife, it's David himself that calls down the sticks and it's David himself that has to deal with them all. But just look at David's office and you can see that he's *not* dealing with them at all. He's just calling down more and more. Eventually there won't be room for any more. Already he's collected enough to make it impossible for anyone to get into his space, so no-one can get close to him. No-one can *help* him. I bet his house is the same, and I bet no-one can get in the door there either."

"So what do we do?" asked Leon. "How can we help him?" Annie looked at him tenderly.

"That's nice, that you want to help someone you've never even met." She put an arm around his waist and pulled him close. "Sadly, I don't think there's much we can do to help him until he clears the way a little and lets us – or someone – get close enough to him to help him cope. The critical part is that *he has to choose to clear the path*. Until then all we can do is be around for when he makes that choice." Without relinquishing her hold on him, she once again set off down the aisle, obliging him to walk in step with her, though it all felt a little awkward, as he didn't know what to do with his arm, trapped as it was between his body and hers. Just when he thought the dilemma was beginning to be troublesome enough to bring him a painstick she let him go, grabbing his fingertips instead.

"You were getting one then" she said, causing him to blush. "A *painstick* I mean!"

she added with a wicked grin, feinting a slap in his direction. He laughed along with her and the two continued on their way in easy silence.

"I've got a question" said Leon after they had progressed some way without seeing another soul. The sounds of the giant office continued to rise around them, but it felt to Leon as though they had found a bubble of privacy in amongst the hubbub. Annie turned to him and nodded.

"Sure. Fire away."

"Lisa..." he halted, not sure how to put his question into words. "When I first arrived this morning... hell, it seems like a *long* time ago, but...this morning, when I was introduced to Lisa I think I might have seen her painsticks. I didn't know what they were at the time of course..."

"Of course" interjected Annie, who was still sure Leon was play-acting his ignorance.

"Anyway...she had them on her desk, but she kind of...swept them up with her hand when I looked towards them, and put them in a drawer in her desk. I think maybe there were some others in there too."

"So what's the question?"

What's *she* doing with her pain, if all she does is stick it in a drawer?"

"She's hiding it, in case someone thinks she's weak. She thinks that if she's not *showing* pain, people will believe that she's not *feeling* pain. Of course, that's rubbish. She's not fooling anyone but herself, but I guess if it makes her feel better then it's doing her some good. The problem is that every time she opens that drawer she sees her pain all over again, and she's not doing anything *with* it, so she's not getting rid of it...not really."

"I think I get it." said Leon "There's another thing too. Another guy had a stack of sticks on his desk. Not a model, like the Basilica guy, just a pile of sticks all criss-crossed, like Jenga..."

"That's pretty common. You'll see that a lot. It's a pyre. People get handed painsticks, but they're for trivial things or at least for things that don't really bother the person, so they stack them, and when the pile gets big enough they set light to it and just *burn* them. Very cathartic. I do it myself sometimes. They smell pretty good when they're burning, and let's face it, what can feel better than seeing something you don't want and no-one else will take from you go up in sweet-scented smoke?"

"I suppose. Makes sense under the circumstances, I...."

"Oh!" Annie interrupted Leon's comment "There's someone I want you to meet. You'll love him! C'mon...down here." she took a sharp left-turn and strode towards a small group of people standing in the walkway a short distance away. As they approached, Leon could hear that they were chatting amicably together and that they all looked relaxed and happy. Annie walked straight into the centre of the group and said:

"Everybody – this is Leon. He just started, so play nice and make him welcome."

The group turned in his direction and Leon was blessed with more than a few warm smiles. One of the men among the group touched him gently on the upper arm.

"Is he in? Are you all waiting?" asked Annie.

One of the group – a woman who looked to be in her 50s – spoke for them all.

"He is and we are, but if you want to skip the queue I don't think anyone will mind." She glanced at her companions as she said this, and received nods of agreement.

"I really just want to introduce Leon to Eddie, so we won't be long."

As Annie said this, a small man wearing a comfortable-looking corduroy jacket exited the workspace carrying a Lilliputian Christmas tree, complete with coloured lights and a small silver star at the top. He was grinning like a kid at...well...at Christmas!

"Annie" whispered Leon. "It's April. What's with the Christmas tree?"

Despite his attempt to be discreet he was overheard by one of the group that surrounded them.

"Oh Eddie doesn't much care what time of year it is. He just loves the whole Christmas thing. He's a year-round Santa! Wait 'til you get inside and meet him."

Annie caught his wrist and pulled him towards the entrance.

"You'll *love* Eddie. Everyone does."

Leon, who shared with many people a deep distrust of being told that he was going to love something or someone felt his hackles rise a little, and was preparing to curl his lip at the 'lovable' Eddie when he caught sight of someone he presumed was this self-same Eddie: a slightly rounded man of maybe 50, with a face so suffused with unmistakeable goodwill that it made sense of Annie's contention that everyone loved him. Leon felt warmed to the core just being in the same space as him, despite his earlier resistance. Eddie smiled broadly.

"Welcome, welcome. A new face! Annie? Who's this? I must say, you make a good looking couple."

Annie blushed, but kept a firm hold of Leon's wrist before sliding her hand down and into his, lacing her fingers with his and leaning into his side a little.

"Eddie," she said, sounding like a teenager introducing a boyfriend to her parents for the first time. "This is Leon. He's new. I wanted him to meet you."

"Well, I'm flattered, young lady. And Leon.." He leaned forward, extending his hand, which Leon shook, surprised at the firmness of the older man's grip, "...it's a real pleasure to meet you. A real pleasure."

While Leon had heard sentiments like this time and again, this time he felt as though it was genuinely meant. He looked Eddie in the eye and said:

"It's a real pleasure to meet you too." And he was a little surprised to find that he meant it!

Eddie looked towards Annie.

"Are there many outside?"

"A few. We jumped the queue, so we mustn't stay."

"Fair enough. Come back and see me properly though. Soon. In the meantime, Leon, I want you to have this. Take it with you and think of me when you look at it."

He handed Leon a duplicate of the miniature tree he had seen in the hands of the corduroy clad man a few minute earlier.

"Thank you" he said, examining the tree, which was wonderfully detailed. He had no idea how the lights worked – there seemed to be nowhere for batteries to go. He held it up to the light and realised that it had been made out of painsticks. Some – the ones that went to make the branches – had been roughed up so that the 'bark' on the outside stood up to emulate pine needles. The whole thing looked like a bonsai Blue Spruce. "Thank you very much!" Again, he surprised himself by how much he meant what he was saying. He knew that if he could see himself in a mirror at that moment he would have been embarrassed by the broad grin that he felt spread across his face.

Annie leant up and kissed Eddie swiftly on the cheek, said goodbye and turned to go, taking Leon with her. As they turned, the young man caught sight of something that had been hidden from view by a filing cabinet when they entered: a larger – indeed a life-sized – version of the tree the Leon was holding. Lights, star, even decorations hanging from some of its branches. All made from carefully crafted painsticks.

"Eddie's on his own...like David," said Annie, as they exited the cubicle and worked their way through the group standing outside. "He lost his wife, two daughters and a son in a plane crash three or four years ago. Unlike David though, he decided he was going to celebrate their lives instead of mourning their deaths. They'd all been on their way to meet him in the Far East for Christmas – he was working in Singapore at the time -- when their plane went down. So now he celebrates Christmas in his own way all year round, and all the pain that comes his way when he thinks of his loss he turns into these trees and shares them with whoever he thinks needs cheering up. When it's *really* Christmas he builds a big tree that stands in the front office."

Leon reflected on this for a moment, and looked once more at his own tree.

"I felt...well...whatever I felt, you were right. I loved him. He just *exudes* personal warmth. I can see why people queue up to see him."

"And your tree might be made out of painsticks, but it's not the same thing at all as having those sticks drop on you, is it?"

"No. It's as though making something 'happy' out of them has changed the pain into something else."

"No" said Annie "It's still pain, but it's pain that's been used creatively to do something more positive. Or with positive intentions, I suppose....after all, it's just a little tree."

"Yeah, but it made *me* feel pretty happy."

Annie looked at him over her shoulder. Then, stopping in her tracks, she turned to face him. She reached out and touched his chest with two fingers, tapping him gently on the breastbone a couple of times."

"You need to be careful," she cautioned. "You're starting to sound like you're enjoying yourself."

"What's not to enjoy?" he retorted. "Here I am with a job, a tiny Christmas tree...in April granted, but nonetheless a beautiful wee tree, and in the company of an intelligent, attractive and witty woman who is also a brilliant teacher, guide and companion."

"And here *I* am, in the company of a gifted, but amateur bullshitter who seems intent on convincing me that he's some sort of visitor from another planet;" all this said with a grin, and therefore – thankfully – not accompanied by any of the dreaded sticks.

"Let's pretend I believe you – just for a moment or two" said Annie, "tell me what it's like...you know...where you live. What do you get if someone's rude to you?"

"You don't 'get' anything. You get on with your life is what you get."

"Well...how do you get rid of your sti...I mean your pain?"

"I don't know. Now I come to think of it, I haven't a clue. Maybe it just sort of...hangs about. Maybe we ignore it."

Annie snorted a little laugh. "You need to do more homework if you're going to make up wacky stories. How do you expect me to believe you when you can't even answer the simplest question about your supposed life?"

"Annie...look...I want to believe in this place, because if it's all just a dream or a hallucination or something, then that would mean that you're not real. And that...that would hurt a lot."

"Plenty of sticks then, if I'm not real?"

"No. No sticks at all...and maybe that would be as hard to cope with as finding out that you and I...that we..."

"You asking me for a dance?"

"What?" Leon was shaken out of his thoughts by her question.

"You were acting like a shy boy at a party, trying to ask a girl for a dance but not knowing how to say it, so I thought I'd lend a hand. If you want to dance with me, then that's just fine. I really like you Leon, and I hope we get to have that dance sometime very soon, but you're giving me a stick or two here yourself...look." She held out her hand to show him a pair of sticks. "That's down to you hanging on to your tale about not knowing what these are."

Leon made a decision.

"You're right. It's just a story. I've been larking about. It's a sort of late April Fool joke. A bit lame I guess. Sorry. Let's forget all about it."

Annie, who should have been delighted by this vindication, suddenly found that she had yet another stick, but couldn't work out exactly why.

"No," she said " let's play along for a bit longer. I promise I won't give you a hard time...just...keep up the game for a bit longer. Until we get you to your desk at least. Is that OK?"

Puzzled by this apparent U-turn, Leon was nonetheless happy to go along with it, knowing that he might learn a little more about the ways people in this strange place dealt with their painsticks, and happy too that he would get to spend more time with Annie. Maybe they would even get that dance!

"We should get on" said Annie. "I've been away from my desk for a while. I expect Stewart's found some way of making the audit thing all my fault by now, and I'll get back to a pile of sticks the size of a small building! Let's get you to...what was it? H12?" Getting a nod of agreement, she continued. "We can cut down here, and take a short-cut through customer services."

The two, once again holding hands – it seemed the natural thing to do – traversed a couple of aisles and turned into a workspace a little bigger than most, with six desks set in a large square, and six people wearing telephone headsets, each talking or listening, while tapping away at keyboards and peering at monitors.

"Customer services" explained Annie. "They get all the service calls and complaints that can't be dealt with online."

Leon assumed that the operators were following scripts or flowcharts on their computers, and thereby dealing with callers as efficiently as possible. He was therefore a little shocked to see that the operator closest to him was actually playing some sort of shoot-'em-up game while apparently listening and responding to a caller. He inched closer so that he could hear at least one side of the conversation.

" I see...yes...yes...no, I'm sure you didn't...yes...uh-huh..."

Leon walked along behind the three operators closest to him and found that they were *all* playing games. In fact, on closer inspection it looked like they were all playing the same game, and, when two of them coincidentally ended their calls at more or less the same time it became apparent that they were actually playing against each other.

"Hahahaaaa...I fragged you good in that tunnel, Chris. You are just *never* going to get anywhere near my base! How many lives have you lost today?"

"Just the two, and I'll get you next time, fat boy – wait and see." Another call came in for each of the two and they once more turned to their calls...and their game.

"Uh-huh...yes...sure...yes...no...yes"

Leon could see that what they were doing was more about letting customers feel that they were getting somewhere rather than actually provide any real service or assistance. He could only imagine how many sticks they were dropping on their callers. He caught Annie's eye and gestured with his head back towards the aisle from which they had entered the space. She followed him out, looking a little puzzled.

"What's up?" she asked, when they were out of sight of the game-playing operators.

"Did you see what they're doing? Did you hear how they were dealing with customers?"

"Yes...it's pretty shabby, but they do provide a service."

"They're playing *computer games* in there! While they're on the phone!"

"I know. But from what I understand, the people who can't get help online mostly just want to have a rant to someone. These guys are there to listen and to make the right sort of noises. Not to actually fix problems. They're not qualified to do that. If they get a sense that there's a real issue, and that it might be best to pass it up the line they transfer the call to one of Anthea's team next door. We can go and see them if you want. They're right next door to where you'll be working."

"Lead on" said Leon and followed Annie's gamine figure back into the gamers' lair and through to the space beyond.

It was clear to Leon as soon as he stepped into the space he assumed was home to 'Anthea's Team' that he had gone about as far – in geographical terms at least – as he could in the vast office complex, for here, for the first time since he entered his new workplace with the HR lady and was introduced to Lisa, there was natural light, rather than the insipid fluorescent lighting that prevailed elsewhere. The large office into which he followed Annie held about 20 desks in a single line, while one wall – behind the backs of the operators who manned the desks – was made up of several large windows set high in the wall. Too high even for Leon, who was taller than average, to see out, but still...natural light!

He turned to Annie, and saw that she too was revelling in the crystalline sunlight. She beamed a huge smile at him.

"Isn't it great? If it wasn't for that..." She tossed her head in the direction of the windows. "I wouldn't mind working here."

Leon looked over to where she had indicated and saw what he had perhaps been too dazzled by the light to spot before: a huge...an *enormous*...pile of pain sticks lying up against the wall, and reaching almost to the windowsills. He turned back to Annie, framing his question as to the origin of this forest of sticks as he did. The question became redundant though, when one of the shirt-sleeved individuals manning the phones finished a call and threw several sticks over his shoulder one after the other, all destined to join the mound of similar objects across the room. As he stood, Leon saw more sticks being flicked backwards from desks along the row.

"What's going on?" he asked.

"These are the guys who take the calls that need some real attention. By the time people have made it through to these guys and girls they've probably spent a couple of hours on the internet and another hour or so on the phone, so when they finally get through, they're not in the best of moods. In fact, most of them are spitting mad! They finally get through to someone who seems to be in some position of authority and they vent. They shout, swear, demand compensation, retribution, revenge, blood...you name it. This team are hand-picked to be able to take all the pain the customer can chuck at them and shrug it off...or more properly, throw it away...over there." She pointed again at the hills and valleys of sticks that had gathered against the wall.

"Does Ellis Ellis know about this treasure trove, I wonder?" said Leon "They'd be en route for Mars by now if they could get hold of these."

"Ha! I never thought of that. Not that I'm going back over there to tell him though."

"Me neither" agreed Leon. The two stood in silence for a moment, contemplating the sheer volume of pain reflected in these stacks and heaps.

Leon reached for Annie's hand.

"I'm not meant to be here Annie." She looked up at him. A small worry-line formed between her eyebrows.

"I can't work in a place where, if you want to see the sun you have to accept a job that means you have to ignore all the pain people want to pile on you. I can't imagine getting to work in time to trek for an hour before I even get to my desk. I don't want to have to carry a compass to find my way to your desk so I can ask you for that dance."

"I understand" she said in a small voice, while she examined the sticks that had just then appeared in her hand.

"No. I don't think you do. Not just yet anyway, but I hope you will shortly. See...I know I said I would keep up the play-acting about not understanding the sticks, but the truth is that I really don't...or rather I *didn't* understand them. I'd truly never seen them or heard of them. No! Don't say anything...let me put my thoughts together." He took a deep, shuddering breath and started once again to talk.

"I know a little about these now" He nodded towards the sticks in her hand. "Thanks to you, and to Eddie, to Lisa and Moustache

Pete. Even Ellis Ellis, I guess. I see that if you can see your pain you can find ways to deal with it...if you choose. You can revel in it like Veronique, or bury yourself in it like David. You can make something beautiful and share it with others, or just keep it for yourself if that's what you want. All the ways of getting rid of them or using them that you've shown me and told me about...it's all been great. A real education. And it's a lesson I could take back to wherever I came from, because it seems to me that it would be just as easy to do all those things with your pain even if there were no sticks. Well...you maybe couldn't build a Saturn 5 rocket, but you can still be creative with your issues and your pain without building models. It might just take a little more imagination, but you *could* build something useful. And for sure if you choose to drown in your sorrow you can do it just as easily without sticks as you can with them.

"What I see now is that it all boils down to recognising that the kind of pain that drops sticks on you here can be recognised, measured, handled and conquered back home where most of us try to ignore it or hide from it until it all gets too big and too scary to avoid or ignore, but by then it's too late to deal with it all easily. If we could do what you do...if we could *see* that pain as it arrived like you do with the sticks, then you could deal with it a little at a time, while it's still manageable.

"What I want to do is somehow see if I really do belong somewhere else. The place I think I remember. The place I think I left behind when I set foot in this office."

With this he turned towards the windows.

"Can you help me with these?" He headed for the nearest pile of sticks. Annie followed.

"Can you climb up on one of these smaller piles?"

"I can try." She clambered up a low stack of sticks, using her hands to scrabble up to the top, then standing -- a little unsteadily -- at the summit. Leon tried to follow, but his weight caused the sticks to start sliding under him and he jumped back to terra firma.

"We need a cloth. Curtains or something like that. Something to hold them in place as we climb."

"What about wedging some chairs into the piles and standing on the chairs?"

"Brilliant!" Leon was as impressed by the fact that Annie hadn't even started to question what he was trying to do as he was by her elegant solution to the problem of making the mountains of sticks stable enough to climb. He followed her out of the office space, suddenly aware that no-one had so much as acknowledged their presence, far less question their actions. He made a mental note to ask Annie, but then decided not to bother. If someone tried to stop them he'd worry about such things then.

Annie meantime had made her way to a storage cupboard in which there were several stacks of conference chairs. She started dragging them into the corridor where Leon busied himself re-stacking them. When they had collected as many as they could feasibly carry or drag they retraced their steps to the office that housed the Anthea's Team, where they continued to be ignored.

Leon took one chair from his stack and placed it on the nearest pile of sticks, leaning on it with all his weight to embed it firmly. He then climbed carefully onto the chair.

"Pass me another one Annie."

The second chair went into a pile a little higher than the first, and Leon inched his way onto it, trying to avoid moving the first chair. Annie raised a third chair high above her head, and Leon stretched down to grab it then turned to place it closer to the windows and a little higher still. He then eased himself backwards off his perch and reversed his route until he once again stood on the floor alongside Annie.

"What we'll do" he explained "is take a chair each, and set them so that they're like stepping stones, but going upwards. They're too far apart as they are."

"OK. I can do one..." She surveyed the scene, picked up a chair and headed for the hills. In short order she had placed a chair so that it made a simple step between Leon's first and second efforts. She then backed down, and Leon took over. One more trip each and they had created an easily traversed ladder reaching to the windows.

"So...now we've re-created an ascent of Everest in miniature, do you want to tell me what exactly it is we're doing?"

"I want to look out of the window. I want to see what the world looks like."

Annie shook her head in mock despair, and gestured with her hand.

"Lead on then, Sir Edmund."

"I don't think he was a Sir until after he got back down."

"Shut up and climb!"

As requested, Leon shut up and began to climb, soon reaching the final chair, which allowed him to easily see over the sill. He turned, and found himself being joined by Annie, who – due to the nature of their perch – had to stand very close to him indeed, and (for reasons of safety) had to put her arm round his waist. He (for similar reasons of safety) wrapped an arm around her shoulders and gently turned her so she could look out on the world.

Spread before them was a beautiful parkland, with short, velvety-looking grass dotted with an occasional tree. The sun shone and the day looked warm and appealing. A few people were walking through or across the meadow, and one couple were sitting on the grass chatting.

"Do you see?" Asked Leon

"See what?"

"No sticks. Twigs firmly attached to trees, and people acting normal."

"You might not see their sticks from here."

"True. But there's only one way to find out." With this Leon grasped the rail at the foot of the window and pulled upwards. After a moment's hesitation, the whole thing lifted, and a breath of sweet fresh air washed over them.

Leon slung one leg over the sill and paused.

"Still want that dance?"

"Certainly do!" came the reply,

"Better come on then, before someone decides to drop one on us."

Afterword

What you've just read is a story. Just that and nothing more complicated than that. However, much of what we learn in life comes from stories of one sort or another, and so it is my hope that you will have recognised something in the course of Leon's journey that resonates with you. Perhaps a character that reminds you of someone in your life or a situation similar to one in which you have found yourself at one time or another.

As you read the story did you find yourself thinking thoughts like "That reminds me of..." or "I know who does that"? Or even "That's me!" If you did, then you will probably already have a better understanding of what you might be carrying around with you as unwanted and unnecessary stress, mental discomfort or anguish.

My belief is that you will carry with you the notion of non-physical pain as something more tangible as a result of having read The Sticking Point, and that you will find within yourself a means by which you can deal more readily with pain that drops on you or that you bring upon yourself, and that as a result you will handle the pain that everyday life inevitably dishes out to us in a timely fashion.

In my working life I frequently see people who carry huge burdens of pain, often without recognising even that it exists, far less acknowledging that it is dragging them down and affecting them in every aspect of their lives.

Since coming up with the ideas that have culminated in the writing of this book I have used the same metaphor of pain sticks with several of these clients, and they have all taken the metaphor and run with it, using it to explain to themselves why they feel as they do, and finding mechanisms by which they can either put their feelings to good use or shrug the negative emotions off.

I hope that you will continue to think about Leon, and people he meets.

If you do, I know that your unconscious mind will work its magic, and you will quickly start to feel differently about the people around you, and your dealings with them, permitting yourself the luxury of leaving your pain sticks behind you and lightening your own burden.

If you like the story, please tell people.

If you 'get' the metaphor, please share it.

If you want to ask a question about any aspect of either the story or the theory behind it, please contact me: steve@stickingpointbook.com

If you would like to engage in more study of some of the background that has gone into this book, then look for work on cognitive behavioural therapy (CBT), gestalt therapy, NLP, metaphor, visualisation and story therapy.

Having said all that, while Leon has his roots in my work in these fields, it's as an amalgam of all of them rather than one specific science or discipline, so your further reading will doubtless take you in many different directions, and may lead you to many different places. Enjoy your journeys!

Acknowledgments

I'd like to thank a few people who were instrumental in helping me bring this book to fruition. Sabina Browne, who was unflaggingly encouraging throughout the process; the committee of Royal Richmond Archery Club for kindly allowing me to use their clubhouse as a writing room when the distractions of the world threatened to drag me away from my self-imposed deadline; my friends and associates at Unlimited Potential Ltd, who gave the notion a fair hearing and a general 'thumbs-up' when I pitched it to them and in particular Tim and Richard Hawkes of the same organisation who gave me all the help I could have asked for; my dear friend Elese Coit in San Diego who let me run the idea past her, and then generously gave her time to read the manuscript and to offer sound advice and sensible criticism. Lee McKenzie and the wonderful Sarah, who found about 3 pages of corrections after I thought I'd made a decent job of fixing the manuscript, Steve Holder, who was so taken by the book that he bought 8 copies to distribute to people he felt would benefit from it. Finally, as in my dedication, I'd like to thank the participants in an unsightly row in the backrooms of a London hospital who set the whole thing in motion, albeit unknowingly. Thanks to you all.

ST. London. 2011

About the author:

Steve Thomson is a coach and trainer of communication and presentation skills for businesses and individuals.

A live event presenter and producer for over 20 years, his business is based on the idea of a professional who trains rather than a professional trainer.

With a keen interest in what makes communication work, Steve has studied and incorporated elements of disciplines as diverse as CBT, aikido, yoga, iMA, singing, NLP and dramatic arts into his training, making his workshops and seminars anything but predictable!

A regular contributor to a number of magazines and websites, this is Steve's first book...but not his last!

Steve lives and works in London, and has clients worldwide.

What's been said about
The Sticking Point

"I'm overwhelmed" Steve Holder,

"It's a little gem, and I hope others far more important than me recognise that"
Lee McKenzie

"Sometimes things come along just when you need them. This wonderful little book did just that" *anon by request*

"Like Kafka – but happy" Tony Stevens

<u>Notes</u>

<u>Notes</u>

<u>Notes</u>

<u>Notes</u>

<u>Notes</u>

Lightning Source UK Ltd.
Milton Keynes UK
UKOW05f0653080614

233041UK00001B/11/P